This illustrated natural history of poisonous plants is a work of haunting beauty and imagination. An evocative text and powerful drawings are combined in complete harmony. Each of these lethal plants is a part of literature, mythology, and the lore of childhood. Esther Baskin deftly weaves curious botanical facts with stories and legends that have accumulated through the centuries about each plant. Poppy, hemlock, deadly nightshade, mandrake and passionflower are part of our familiar world but are given new dramatic meaning by Leonard and Esther Baskin.

THE
POPPY
AND
OTHER
DEADLY PLANTS

BY ESTHER BASKIN

DRAWINGS BY LEONARD BASKIN

A SEYMOUR LAWRENCE BOOK

DELACORTE PRESS

NEW YORK

Books by Leonard and Esther Baskin
Creatures of Darkness
The Poppy and Other Deadly Plants

To Toby

who fearfully frightened me

by eating a berry of

Solanum dulcamara

which grew near our porch.

To Sid.

CONTENTS

PREFACE

The early history of poisonous plants is shrouded in myth. Medea knew them after Hecate first explored their usage. The ancient Greeks and Romans did not consider it dishonorable to commit suicide with them. Also, the Egyptians understood well how to do away with unwanted ones by using ruinous remedies.

Dioscorides (40-90 A.D.), Greek natural historian, discoursed about plant and other sickening poisons. Particularly, he wrote about substances like the solanums, aconite and the precious opium, as well as about minerals such as cinnabar (mercury) and arsenic. Pliny also mentions these deadly things and their orders. The early herbalists, in manuscript and printed book, illustrated with woodcut or engraving, as in Dodoens or Gerard, wrote about many wondrous plants and, here and there, about some beastly ones.

The plants discussed in these pages are not like the wily poison ivy, which only causes nasty itching, but rather those which really kill people. And kill them with a fury.

I. POPPY

Paper-thin is the flimsy, flickering petal of the poppy's red, red flower. It stains objects that encroach upon it with a pale red blotch. Never mind the white and pink ones, we'll talk mostly of the fiery red one, the one that is planted and grows tall in gardens.

Wondrous opium, the powerful narcotic that eases pain and brings tender rest and sleep (and sometimes death if carelessly taken), comes from the poppy.

It has a hard-bound, woody, brittle and greenish-white long root which dies as soon as the fruit is ripe. Straight and hairy is the stalk, which rises to about five feet and contains a bud or button with a few branches on the top. There are five greenish white leaves, more or less, large, hairy, and broad. (The coloring of the leaves of the horned or thorny poppy is quite otherwise. They are streaked with milky-white veins or ribs, which make it look a lot like Our-Lady's-thistle. Hairy and rough-cloven, the leaves are prickled with tiny, cruel thorns, thus its name.) The poppy's wide leaves, each with a purplish blotch on its bottom, flop on the ground. The leaves are rent, toothed, jagged or snipped around the edges. Roundish and ashen-colored are its small seeds, which, if allowed to shed on the ground, would give birth to flowers next year untrue as to color. Jules Verne tells us, in *The Mysterious Island*, that the poppy's capsuled head has a total of 3,200 seeds!

Central to the poppy is its charcoal-colored, seeded, pitlike heart. The round bowl of the head is wrapped or folded in a thin, scaly skin and bows down shamefacedly before it blooms. A star-like cover, a striped and thready crown or chaplet, encloses the head in which the many capsules, as they ripen, are partitioned into single cells which contain the seeds. One remembers how, in the fall, florists display many dried flowers, including poppy heads or seed capsules, that rattle or jangle.

The poppy's head can become as grand as an apple and holds the fluid that is the powerful opium. Every part of the plant, stalk, leaf and head, particularly when young and green, when crushed, yields the milky juice, which is quite corrosive. It is opium, and it has a heady odor, a foul taste, but, worse yet, causes nausea and vomiting.

Its red flower sings gloriously. But then one must admit that it has other colors, white, rose, purple-blackish, blue and murrey or tawny, and the flowers come single and double. The folded petals embrace the head; they have fine hirsute threads with little tips at the end, and are scarified about the edges, looking like windblown feathers.

We speak now of a few things about the poppy, leaving botany behind. Going back to the ancient Greeks, the goddess Ceres, also known as Demeter, after her daughter Proserpine was carried off by Pluto to the nethermost reaches of Hades, wept inconsolably for her return. In her grief, to reconcile herself to the absence of Proserpine, she invented opium draughts to help sleep off her despair.

Sir Thomas Browne composed a poem on this myth:

> *Sleep-bringing Poppy, by the plowman late,*
> *Not without cause to Ceres consecrate. . . .*
> *Fairest Proserpine was rapt away,*
> *And she in plaints the night, in tears the day*
> *Had long time spent: when no high power could give her*
> *Any redresse, the Poppy did relieve her:*
> *For eating of the seeds, they sleep procured,*
> *And so beguiled those griefs she long endured.*

The thirteenth-century philosopher-poet Fra Bartholomaeus Anglicus called opium that ''slepi herbe.''

In our day, Lyman Frank Baum has written of the soporific effects of the poppy upon his heroine. In *The Wizard of Oz,* going through a field of flowers, Dorothy comes to a patch of poppies. She falls dead asleep from the plant's dreamy vapor, and sleeps on until rescued from the heady meadow.

In ancient times the corn rose (a poppy) was garlanded along with

barley, bearded wheat, and corn, and used as a good-luck offering for the well-being of the corn, with the poppy's multifarious seeds presented as a worshipful token to Ceres. The goddess is often pictured holding poppies in her hands, as do the lesser gods, Hypnos (Sleep), Thanatos (Death), and Nyx (Night), all of quiescent renown, who are crowned with poppies in their hair.

Ancient astrologers said the poppy was a flower worthily representing the yellow moon.

The early Assyrians used opium as a remedy for "broken toes," of all things. What they did was rub the toe with opium and fat, and then bandage it. Surely it was the opium that did the work and not the fat. They also used the root of the poppy as a love potion. The Babylonian king Merodach-baladan, in a tablet, says that the poppy growing in his garden, with its many seeds, represented fruitfulness rather than sleep.

Lethean was the name Virgil bestowed on the poppy, which he found fit to be presented in a funeral rite given to Orpheus. It was also typical of the Romans to place poppies on the bier as they prayed intently for the pacification of malign beings. Pliny tells us how to collect raw opium but then warns us that "taken in too large quantities it is productive of sleep unto death even." Dioscorides says that "being drunk too much . . . it kills."

There is a magical business having to do with lovers and the poppy. Their faithfulness was attested to by the flower's special performance in the lover's hands. Placing a poppy leaf or petal in the palm and hitting it with the other hand meant faithfulness if it snapped back with a sharp retort, but unfaithfulness if it was limp. This superstition was practiced in Greece, Italy, and Switzerland, and was framed into a poem by the early Greek poet Theocritus, thus:

> *By a prophetic Poppy leaf I found*
> *Your changed affection, for it gave no sound,*
> *Though in my hand struck hollow as it lay,*
> *But quickly withered like your love away.*

Hippocrates said that opium could be a strengthening and nourishing bit of one's diet. Theophrastus, the philosopher and father of botany, gave a very clear report of the poppy plant but said of its medicinal qualities only that it "purgd downward" —whatever that meant —but some of the Greeks knew well that opium was a potent medicine leading to sleep and perhaps death, and when they did not acknowledge this truth, Greek mythology surely did.

Paracelsus, the controversial figure who called himself "greater than Celsus," was the inventor of laudanum, mostly made from opium, distilled water and alcohol, and originally an expensive way of taking the drug. A bit of a charlatan, he gave this prescription for his medicine: it should contain "a quarter of its weight in opium to which was added henbane juice, mummy, salts of pearls and corals, the bone of the heart of a stag, bezoar stone, amber, musk, unicorn and some spices, with a few drops of many of the essential oils." Soon everyone realized that "unicorn" and "mummy" were not really important but that opium was.

There is a fourteenth-century medical manuscript that mentions a prescription for making a sleeping draught called "dwale" or, as we know it, opium. And it is so called by Chaucer, in "The Reeve's Tale":

Ther was na more hem neded no dwale
This miller hath so wisly bidded ale,
That as an hors he snorteth in his sleep. . . .

In early medical manuscripts "dwale" is mentioned as a drink "to make a man slepen-en whyle men kerve hym." A good way to effect surgery and "safly kerven hym" was to deaden a man's consciousness and put him into a drunken stupor until the butchery was done, and so opium helped to "kerven." This was all done by boiling the opium in "the gall of a boar" or, for a female patient, in the gall of a spayed sow!

Opium is both an evil and potent drug but also a good and tender medicine, so one can say it is like the flame that both warms and dangerously hurts. We should surely honor the doctor who thought of using opium as an anesthetic, because when judiciously administered it leads one to a gentle, necessary sleep.

Many are the quacks who knew how to carry on well with the gifted opium that led to poisonous dreams.

In the early days of the Industrial Revolution, Elizabeth Kent wrote in her *Flora Domestica* (1832) about something called "Godfrey's Cordial." After the men were thrown out of work by the chaotic times, they found it was cheaper to spend their few coppers for opium cordial rather than for bread and meat. According to Wooten in his *Chronicles of Pharmacy,* Godfrey's nostrum was still popular in the early part of the twentieth century. Miss Kent goes on to speak of laudanum as being "so much used instead of tea by the poorer class of females in Manchester and other manufacturing towns and not unknown to the same class in London as a gentle sedative and the inducer of oblivious delirium from the cares of life."

So many quacks there were who, often as mountebanks, traveled far and wide selling their nostrums and working with a helpful aid or zany. The zany, also called a "Merry-Andrew," dressed himself in delightful clothing, diapered and particolored, and acted the clown. The word "mountebank" originally meant a man who mounted a bank or bench and cried forth his wares therefrom.

Opium was a mainstay of quackdom even though the quack mixed it with nonsensical stuff for medicine. But nothing did so well as opium. A famous quack was Spot Ward, so called because he had a birthmark on his face. He miraculously cured his sovereign, George II, of a dislocated thumb, using the good opium as well as ipecac and other ineffectual drugs. Alexander Pope directed one of his barbed couplets at Ward:

> *Of late without the least pretense to skill*
> *Ward's grown a famed physician by a pill.*

Continental monks put together many drugs and, of course, some laced with opium. One that strongly breathed forth opium was called "Baume Tranquille," made by the Capucines, and Madame de Sévigné always kept a dollop of it with her because it was scarce, only a little bit of it being made at a time.

The quacks exploited the healing use of opium, dangerously. (In our country, only the Pure Food and Drug Acts did away with these madnesses.)

In the Napoleonic wars after the fields at Waterloo were filled with corpses following Wellington's murderous and glorious victory, it was said that red poppies came from the blood of the fallen.

Armistice Day is otherwise known as Poppy Day because of the prevalence of poppies growing on the murderous battlefields, as in Flanders. So war and poppies come together again in this poem, an old saw, by John McCrae:

In Flanders fields the poppies blow
Between the crosses, row on row,
That mark our place: and in the sky
The larks still singing bravely fly,
Scarce heard amid the guns below.

We are the dead. Short days ago
We lived, felt dawn, saw sunset glow,
Loved and were loved, and now we lie
    In Flanders fields.

Take up our quarrel with the foe!
To you, from failing hands we throw
The torch—be yours to hold it high!
If ye break faith with us who die,
We shall not sleep, though poppies grow
    In Flanders fields.

We know that wars usually have an underlying cause, and this war we write of now was provoked by the poppy. China wished to have nothing to do with the Western "barbarians," but it was not her own hong merchants who sold opium to the Chinese. It was rather the British East India Company that illegally imported the drug into China and then introduced that country to a vicious and pernicious addiction to opium.

England had Waterloo well behind her, so now she could open fire on China, and she did. In the peace treaty of 1908, when crown colonies became free traders with China, although the opium trade was forbidden, the English had already sown their evil, and, in fact, continued sub rosa. Such is the ugly story of the Opium War.

And now for a fable. This is a "once upon a time" tale. On the banks of the river Ganga lived a Bengali seer who had a pet mouse which he changed into a cat for fear of losing him. The cat was then transformed into a series of different animals—a dog, an ape, a boar—each time to enable it to escape another beast hostile to itself, and finally ended up by being changed into a regal princess, called the Poppy-seed Lady, whom a king fell in love with and married. One day the princess was watering her plants, and, becoming dizzy, she fell into the nearby well and there died. Then the seer or rishi had the well filled with earth, from which sprang up the poppy plant. The rishi then said that the opium smoker would have the qualities of the animals the mouse had been changed into: frolicsome like the original mouse, loving milk like a cat, fighting like a dog, loathsome like an ape, fierce like a boar, and finally, majestic like a queen.

A few eighteenth- and nineteenth-century English writers were opium addicts as well as bookish heroes. There is Coleridge, who is said to have written his wondrous poem, "Kubla Khan," after falling into a deep sleepy dream from a draught of opium. Perhaps "The Rime of the Ancient Mariner" was written under its influence. Opium was also taken by George Crabbe, the poet, who felt that it was the "inducer of delicious delirium" He kept near his bed a lamp and a pencil so he could compose upon waking from his opium dream. Thomas De Quincy, in his *Confessions of an English Opium-Eater,* tells us he had become mad with neuralgia afflicting his head and face and walked the streets of London to forget the pain. He met an old friend who told him to take laudanum to ease his misery. After De Quincy swallowed the tincture of opium, he joyously said: ". . . in an hour, O heavens! . . . what a resurrection!

what an apocalypse of the world within me! That my pains had vanished was now a trifle . . . swallowed up in the immensity . . . of divine enjoyment thus suddenly revealed . . . here was the secret of happiness . . . happiness might now be bought for a penny and carried in the waistcoat pocket. . . ."

Branwell Brontë, the brother of those noble and melancholy sisters, was a gay blade but a ne'er-do-well who drank too much and took opium.

Francis Thompson, in a poem written to "The Poppy," says this:

> *All that the world of me esteems,*
> *My wither'd dreams, my wither'd dreams.*

And we know what makes dreams vivid and not "wither'd."

Perhaps Conan Doyle himself smoked opium — he seemed to know enough about it — for he had Sherlock Homes take it. And once again, Jules Verne. In *Around the World in Eighty Days,* in a den in Hong Kong a group of people fall dead asleep from the narcotic opium after smoking it in long clay pipes and taking it in pellets dissolved in essence of rose water, while drinking gin and stout. In the incomplete story by Charles Dickens *The Mystery of Edwin Drood,* the pianist, Mr. Jasper, who appears as a foul hero, smokes the wicked pipe along with Edwin Drood. Another Dickens' book where opium figures heavily is *Oliver Twist.* A dying drone, who has procured opium from her apothecary, takes it along with gin, but it doesn't help her. She sadly passes away. In the same book there is a raucous and ghastly robber called Bill Sikes who is terribly sick and sleeps only after taking laudanum.

These are only some of the many books with opium-addicted characters. We'll let the others sleep.

Morphine and codeine are two useful products very closely related to opium. The poppy plant's gifted codeine was at one time (not now, we hope) nastily given by mothers to hush a child's irksome crying. Better let the babies cry.

A good way to end this piece is with a passage from Shakespeare:

Nor poppy, nor mandragora,
Nor all the drowsy syrops of the world,
Shall ever medicine thee to that sweet sleep
Which thou ow'dst yesterday.

II. HELLEBORE

The flower of black hellebore blooms around Christmastime, so it is called the Christmas rose, flowering amidst the snow and vying with the snow's brightness. It is an evergreen plant with dark-green, glossy leaves and expanding, large white or purplish flowers. In its hollow heart are pieces like ears. If the weather be temperate and mild, it flowers ever more brightly. Growing on the borders of woods and thickets in the upper crust of the earth and in chalky soil, the thick, rather succulent stems rise to a height of one or two feet, bearing numerous spreading, stalked, hardy leaves, snipped sharply about. They are divided like fingers, hang like a vine, and resemble the plane tree's leaves, serrated or toothed like a saw on the edges. The many rather pendulous, belly-like, oval-shaped flowers, each as big as a nickel, are cup-formed and composed of five rounded, concave, green sepals, tipped with purple, containing several small, tubular petals.

The hellebore has a fibrous, barklike root which consists of a great number of brownish-black strings or threads, woven or inter-laced, running deep into the ground. The root, with only a little bit of moisture or sap in it, is strongly fastened to a thick head, the breadth of a thumb. From the root rise several fair green leaves, each looking much like a skin, nicked and dented, and resembling field ranunculus, crowfoot, or cranesbill. The leaves stand on thick, round, stiff, green and short foot-stalks, and are plaited with eminent ribs overlapping one another at the bottom.

The flowers are thick, dashed with purple about the brims, and set together with tufts or umbels hiding under the leaves. In the middle of the flower are many pale yellow threads or thrums stand-

ing upon a green head (which resembles a columbine's) and which afterwards grows to be the seed vessel. This vessel is divided into several cells or pods, rather like horns, and contains somewhat long and round blackish seeds which look like wheat.

The hellebore has a terrible odor and sad-looking leaves. It is known to kill worms but it rather often kills the person who has taken some of it as a purging, worm-killing medicine, when given by an imprudent hand. Salmon, an eighteenth-century herbalist, tells how as a child he wandered into a waste field and tasted the hellebore growing wild there. It was only a bit, which luckily did not poison him, even though the danger was great. It worked strangely, for it made him lose all the hair of his head and body, the nails of his feet and hands, and every square inch of skin, which peeled right off.

Hellebore has a curious history. The Christmas rose is also called Melampodium, after Melampus, who lived at Pylos in Peloponnesus about 1,500 years before the birth of Christ. He went to Egypt, then the center of science, and studied medicine. One thing he discovered, amongst others, was the cathartic properties of hellebore, after seeing how it worked upon goats which had eaten it. The daughters of Proteus, King of Argos, had their madness cured by Melampus when he had them bathe in a cold bath sprinkled with the juice of hellebore. But Pliny has said that Melampus really gave them the milk of goats which had eaten the herb.

Because hellebore was such a successful medicine it was placed in every pharmacopoeia and the masses thought of it with superstitious belief. It was thought to be good for sanctifying houses, and was used to spray and perfume places to keep away evil spirits. The plant was celebrated with religious feeling, and earnest hymns were chanted to it. The virtues of hellebore were used to bless the kine and it also kept away the spells of the malevolent. The root was unearthed with ritualistic fanfare. Those who believed in it drew a circle around the plant with a sword; then, facing the east, they offered a prayer to Apollo and Aesculapius as they dug up the root.

While all this was going on, the careening and soaring of the eagle were nervously observed as an omen, for its movements could mean the assured, sinister death of anyone who had plucked the plant for his use during the year.

Hellebore used to be very common in the port of Anticyra on the Gulf of Corinth, so, "Sail to Anticyra" (*Naviga ad Anticyram*) was an ordinary saying given to hypochondriacal people, because hellebore, growing prominently there, was certain to sicken them.

Pausanias recalls that, when Athens was besieged by the Cirrhaeans, Solon counseled that, should hellebore be tossed in the river Plistus, the Cirrhaeans, upon swallowing the river's water, would be so given to attacks of dysentery that they would not be able to do battle.

Ancient astrologers felt that hellebore was an evil herb of Saturn, the Roman agricultural god.

The Gauls are said to have invariably rubbed the points of their arrows with hellebore, believing that it made the game tender.

In digging up the roots of certain species of hellebore, it has been thought necessary to eat garlic previously, to counteract the poisonous effluvia of the plant. Also, the root was eventually dried and pounded to dust, in which state it was taken in the manner of snuff.

R. Turner, astrologer and botanist, writing in 1663, says that at that time hellebore was thought to cure those who seemed possessed by the devil, and therefore was by some called *Fuga Demonum.*

Hellebore has long been considered a plant of evil omen, growing in dark and lonely places. Thus the eighteenth-century poet Thomas Campbell says of it:

> *By the witches' tower*
> *Where hellebore and hemlock seem to weave*
> *Round its dark vaults a melancholy bower*
> *For spirits of the dead at night's enchanted hour.*

This plant, with certain accompanying exorcisms, was reputed to be efficacious in cases of deafness caused by witchcraft.

In his *Anatomy of Melancholy,* Burton introduces the hellebore among the emblematical figures of his frontispiece, with the following lines:

> *Borage and hellebore fill two scenes,*
> *Sovereign plants to purge the veins*
> *Of Melancholy, and cheer the heart*
> *Of those black fumes which make it smart;*
> *To clear the brain of misty fogs,*
> *Which dull our senses, and soul clogs;*
> *The best medicine that e'er God made*
> *For this malady, if well assaid.*

III. MAD APPLE

Like the deadly nightshade this is a *Solanum*, not *Solanum lethale*, thank God, but almost as bad. Winter frosts kill it and it lasts only until the snow falls. Its root has many strings attached to it, some small, others big, but it doesn't bury itself deep in the ground. From the root, covered with lacelike threads, rise up hard, round, brownish-green stalks about two feet high. Then come many vine-like branches. The leaves, broad, hairy and pointed, look like those of henbane or of deadly nightshade; later, on short stems sprout forth several large flowers of a sickening, purplish-white hue with many yellow filaments in the center. The flower has six parts and looks like a star. It is very large and generally of an ashen gray or wan color, but some can be much more colorful. Cupped in the husk is the fruit—white, yellow, or brown as a chestnut, with a thin skin or peel, like a shell, around it—as big as a goose's or swan's egg, yet more like a cucumber in the quantity of seeds. This fruit is full of a white pulp or juice, with many small, flat, whitish seeds; the whitish-green cup is jagged.

In the West Indies the mad apple is broiled and eaten with salt and pepper, and it is very much relished in the eastern parts of the world. It is called brown-John or brown-jolly by the dwellers of the British West Indies. Some botanists call it the larger-fruited nightshade, as it is.

Melanzana is a name given to it by the Italians, a corruption of the ancient Latin, *Mala insana*. Whereas it was called by the English of old, raging apple or mad apple (as we know it today), by the Spanish it is called *berenjena*. And it has many other foreign names, the Orientals knowing it as melongena, or biningan, or brinjal.

Gerard says of this plant: "Doubtless these apples have a mischievous qualitie, the use whereof is utterly to bee forsaken."

Until the nineteenth century, the mad apple was thought to be highly poisonous. It is now apparent that only the vine is toxic. Humans continue to enjoy the fruit by the rather less dangerous name of eggplant.

IV. HEMLOCK

Hemlock is very often thought of as a tree (and, of course, it is a conifer), but it is also the name of a poisonous plant (which brought on Socrates' creeping official death). The plant has no relation to the tree.

Hemlock has a long, white, hollow, and somewhat crooked and tapering root, which is like that of parsnip or carrot, and a hollow green stem. This stem, when sucked on and blown like a horn by children at play, leads at times to unwelcome death. Shiny and glistening is its tall stalk, which reaches a height of three or four feet. The stem is coated with gross red spots and has joints from which spring forth large winged leaves, one resting upon the other, serrated at the edges, and of a dreary, glassy green color. There is some twiggery on top, and the white clustered inflorescent umbell is in the center. The seed or fruit, which comes after the flower has gone by, is long, white and flat, with notched edges.

The hemlock grows comfortably in waste fields near walled hedges, amidst weedy garden lots, and in untilled soil. Sometimes it is green all winter long, sometimes not, depending on the climate. The water hemlock, growing in moist, marshy and miry places, is just as poisonous. In France it is known euphemistically as deadtongue because of its paralyzing effect upon the voice.

Hemlock has a horrendously offensive smell and all parts of the plant carry this odor, especially when it is bruised and crushed. The stench is a lot like that of a foul mouse, so said a doctor.

It is remarked in a pharmacopoeia that many diseases can be cured by bits of hemlock or infusions thereof.

Amongst the ancient philosophers of Greece, a regal way of dying for those who had committed "offenses" was to crown themselves with a garland of flowers, then, with a brave smile on their lips, hating the infirmities and weariness of old age and still respected as men of fortitude, they gulped the hemlock of their own free will. So died Theramenes and Phocion.

Chafing themselves with hemlock the Eleusinian priests made themselves pure, they felt. After this they believed nothing could go counter to their oracles.

Pliny remarks that snakes crawl away from hemlock's unearthly hairy parts, because it is botanically a "cold" plant which literally chills to death, and snakes hate cold.

Like hellebore, hemlock is considered a Satanic herb. In Russia it is called *Beh*; and in Germany it is thought of as a funereal plant of the nether regions. Some English writers superstitiously hold it to be a witches' herb and an ill omen, sprouting in dumps and waste fields, and used in their evil odoriferous elixirs.

The Hebrew prophet Hosea has this to say about our ominous plant: "Judgment springeth up as Hemlock in the furrows of the field."

In the fall, the dried, hollow stalks of hemlock rustle in the wind like scarecrows, and the English country folk onomatopoetically call them kecksies, or kex.

Keats, in his "Ode to a Nightingale," speaks in passing of this deadly plant:

> *A drowsy numbness pains my sense*
> *As though of hemlock I had drunk.*

V. MANDRAKE

The root of the mandrake is its most telling part and much of the herb's medicinal goodness comes from it. The mandrake is called male and female, not for botanic reasons, not because of the female pistil and the male stamen, but because the root of the male resembles a man's thighs and legs while the root of the female resembles a woman's. The mandrake is said to utter a human shriek when pulled out of the earth.

If one thinks of the mandrake root anthropomorphically, then it can be said that its one long root has a head and body, although sometimes the root is divided into two legs. This long thick root, to which are joined several small thready fibers, runs deeply into the ground and looks like a radish; its coloring is usually almost black on the outside and white within; sometimes the entire male plant is white and the female black.

There are differences between the male and female mandrake. The odor of the fruit is more suffocating or heady in the male, less obnoxious in the female. This is not true of the leaves. Although some early herbals hold to a contrary view of the notion expressed here about odors, it is safer to believe the later ones. Then, too, the female apple or fruit is paler and smaller (as the root is) than the male. And the seeds of the female are much smaller, blacker and flatter than the male's. The mandrake has many large, thick, light-green leaves, very much resembling a beet's. The female leaf has certain other differences from the male; it is smaller, narrower, shinier and of a darker green color, crumpled and lying on the ground. Keep in mind that the leaves resemble those of a lettuce; don't bring them into the kitchen.

These wide, pointed leaves rise up on slender, smooth stems or foot-stalks, as do the greenish white husks, topped by the flower, which is of a bluish-purplish color, particularly in the female. After the flower, as in other such plants, comes the golden apple, as large as a pippin, smooth, round and shining, and looking not like a pear, as some herbalists have said, but more like the golden Delicious apple.

There are many legends and tales and much lore and poetry about the mandrake as well as special Latin names for it. *Atropa mandragora* comes from Atropos, one of the Parcae, the gods that control fate, the life and death of mankind. Atropos would gather up her black somber robes, then from the clue of threads would draw, measure and cut with a scissors a length of thread which would represent the fated person's lifeline. *Atropa mandragora* is closely related to *Atropa belladonna*, the deadly nightshade. Another name was given by Dioscorides, who called it *Circeium,* after Circe, daughter of Helios and Perse, the great enchantress who, with her sirens, enticed Odysseus and his men, and used many venomous herbs, as well as magic and witchcraft, to further ensnare them. It was also given the name of *Anthropomorphos* by Pythagoras, the fifth-century (B.C.) Greek philosopher, who was said to call it the *forma humana,* as people superstitiously found its twisted root to resemble the human form, with breast, belly and two legs.

In the time of the Hebrews, it was held in high esteem; but not as a mere vegetable, for it was said to keep off sterility. Hence Rachel desired the mandrake plant, and Reuben brought it to his mother, Leah. The Hebrews called it *Dudaim.* In the East it was said to be an aphrodisiac—a mystic plant, coated with an evil spirit supposed to stimulate the passions.

The Romans muttered superstitious incantations over the mandrake root. Pliny states that, before it was dug up, they enacted certain ceremonies. Making sure the wind was at their backs, they would make three circles around the plant with the point of the sword, and then face the west.

Only because the mandrake had such health-giving and favorable narcotic properties could such a dangerous plant be dug up.

The malignant quality of this horrific herb was its great evil power to do terrible ills even unto death-dealing and none felt it safe to tear out the root from its earthen couch. To protect oneself from woe, the neighboring earth was dug up and the dangerous herb was attached to the tail of a dog, which was then chased away, and so the root was yanked out. Thus the poet Andrew Marvell says: "If they have a mind to pull up that mandrake, it were advisable . . . to chuse out a dog for that imployment."

In an Anglo-Saxon manuscript of the tenth or eleventh century, the mandrake figures as a mystic plant that is incandescent at night, lit like a candle. Because of this enchanted evening glow the Arabs, out of their dreams, called it the devil's candle. Thinking of its strange shining look, Thomas Moore versified, in *Lalla Rookh*, about the weird effusion:

> Such rank and deadly lustre dwells,
> As in those hellish fires that light
> The Mandrake's charnel leaves at night.

Mandrake was also said to thrive in the gloom of the gallows, to take root in the breath and flesh of criminals executed on the gibbet. When uprooted, certain writers tell us, it uttered sensitive shrieks and almost human moans. Shakespeare speaks of this sad call:

> Would curses kill, as doth the Mandrake's groan,
> I would invent as bitter-searching terms,
> As curst, and harsh, and horrible to hear.

These screeching noises were so terrifying that Shakespeare tells us in another place that their result was to drive one berserk.

> And shrieks like Mandrakes, torn out of the earth,
> That living mortals, hearing them, ran mad.

Moore tells us of still another poetic notion about the mandrake's shrieks:

> The phantom shapes—oh touch them not—
> That appal the maiden's sight,
> Lurk in the fleshy Mandrake's stem
> That shrieks when plucked at night.

Columella, the poet, arranged for the positioning of his garden in such a way that

> The Mandrakes flowers
> Produce, whose root shows half a man, whose juice
> With madness strikes.

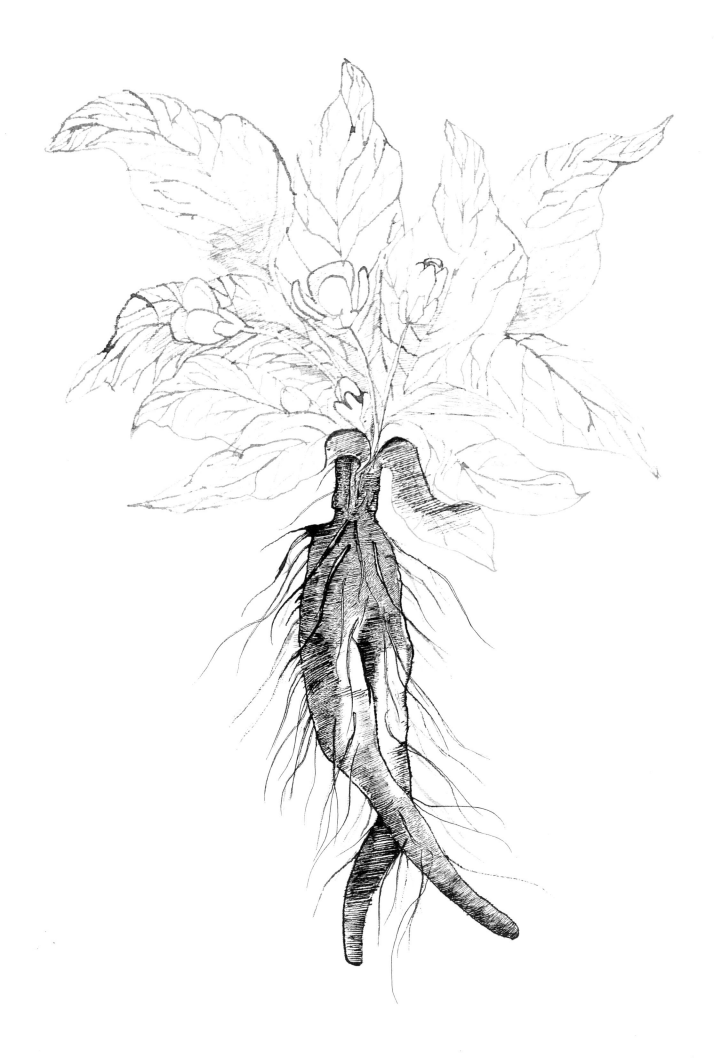

And here is a part of a great poem by John Donne:

Goe, and catche a falling starre,
Get with child a mandrake root,
Tell me, where all past yeares are,
Or who cleft the Divels foot.

Then there are some very old and funny medicinal notions, such as this one from Lyly's *Euphues:* "Your sonne Memphis, had a moale under his eare. . . . You shall see it taken away with the juyce of mandrage." And this line from the writer and rector Edward Topsell: "Oyl of Mandrag . . . bindeth together . . . bones being either shivered or broken."

In his *Natural History,* Bacon says this of the mandrake: "Some plants there are, but rare, that have a mossie or downie root, and likewise that have a number of threads, like beards, as Mandrakes, whereof witches and impostours make an ugly image, giving it the forme of a face at the top of the root, and leave those strings to make a broad beard down to the foot."

Comtesse de Genlis, a French author, recounts a tale about the mandrake, its root being made into the shapes of little idols, all mysteriously wrapped in a piece of cloth, and bringing good fortune. Mandrake, as we know, was called mandragora, and this was also the name of the mythic little sprite hatched from an egg in such a way that the small monster (half-chick and half-man) had to be spirited away to a hidden room and fed the seed of spikenard, after which it could prophesy. In an occult way, mandrake was supposed to make its owner fortunate at sport, finding wealth everywhere and foreseeing the future.

The believing folk of various countries held to a conviction that the root of mandrake, if pulled up from the soil, grew to be a favorable spirit belonging to its owner, a spirit that cured many illnesses and found the way to private riches. It could double the wealth contained in a chest, hold back harsh spirits, perform as a love charm, and accomplish other noteworthy duties.

In Germany, during the period of the Goths, the word *alruna* meant both witch and mandrake. Like the French peasants, the Germans made the root into small images or idols which they treated as oracles. In England, during Henry the Eighth's time, many were made and sold in safe containers, and they had steady buyers.

In Italy the peasants once thought that they could find the shape of a man in the leaves of the mandrake and a physiognomy in its roots. In a hot sand-bath the cut-up roots of white briony, formed like figures of men and women, were said to be put there by sellers who faked them as mandrake roots.

French people call the mandrake *main de gloire* or *maglore* and the superstitious peasantry used to call it an enchanted elf. The peasant also thought that the mandrake was a kind of mole and that the person who discovered it had to give it something to eat, bread, or meat, or some other kind of victual, and that it had to have the same quantity of food every day. If not, the mandrake would cause the neglectful one to die. To reward the unneglectful, the *main de gloire* would give back twice what it had received the day before. When one had paid for its food with cash, then the money would be doubled soon after. "Thou horson [whore son] Mandrake," Shakespeare called it.

VI. DARNEL

Resembling a forage plant like corn or barley, darnel stands loftily. It has a bunchy fibrous root from which emerge culms or stems with strake-like plates much like thick knees. From the oaten, winged, spiky head sprouts ripe grain with sharp, short-pointed awns or bearded, scabrous sheaths, which are somewhat reddish. Then come the rough chaffy husks or glumes. The seeds or tares are easily shaken out of the ears, which are small, tender and flat.

Darnel is about four feet high and it has rather narrow leaves each with a kind of prickly tongue, or at times little leaflets or

rachises, and no real florescence other than its grasslike wheaten face.

Like other "deadly" plants, darnel is both a medicine and a poison. Pliny states that Virgil called darnel "unfruitful" and said that when it is ground and boiled in vinegar it cures impetigo and helps the more often the application is changed. Darnel meal also serves to remove splinters from bone.

"To subsist on darnel" idiomatically once meant "to have bad eyes." In the sixteenth century, there is a line written by one J. Jones: "Some darnell is crepte in amongst the godd corne." Another statement about darnel shows what happens when it is lost in the wheat: "But while men slept, his enemies came and sowed tares among the wheat." The English call wheat corn; thus this line from the poet Dryden: "Oats and Darnel choak the rising corn." Sometimes, when bread is made, the wheat is unfortunately mixed in with darnel seed. This crystalline, dirty-white substance is eaten in the bread and the eater staggers about as if drunk. The metaphorical possibilities of darnel, creeping in among the wheat and barley, inspired many a writer. H. Barrow, in the sixteenth century, mentions: "Satan sowing his darnel of errors and tares of discord among them." Still another writer of the same century, Foxe, mentions "the detestable darnel of desperation." "A graine of good corne in a great deal of darnell" —says the seventeenth-century writer J. Ball, whose contemporary, Holland, also mixes wheat with darnel: "Darnell floure laid too, with Oxymell [a kind of vinegar and honey solution], cureth the gout."

There are parables in the New Testament about darnel and its tares. In Matthew (xiii : 38) Jesus preaches: "The field is the world; the good seed are the children of the kingdom; but the tares are the children of the wicked one."

VII. DEADLY NIGHTSHADE

Once my young boy, Toby, ate some red berries near the porch. He swallowed but did not chew them. With relief, I found out that those berries were from the *Solanum dulcamara* (bittersweet nightshade) and not from the *Solanum lethale* (deadly nightshade). Had he chewed them, they could have given him a bad bellyache; had he swallowed them without chewing, very little trouble. The *dulcamara* tastes sweet, unlike the *lethale,* of which Salmon says: "... The whole plant has no good taste nor smell, but unsavory, bitter, and very pernicious" —like the evil flowers in Hawthorne's Rappaccini's garden. (The breath and touch of Rappaccini's daughter, poisoned by her father's corrupt blooms, withered the flowers and insects with which she came into contact.)

The berries of deadly nightshade are green in the early summer and when ripe in August are a shiny black color like polished jet, and full of purplish juice and whitish seeds. The root is great and grows deep in the ground with many spreading branches. The plant rises to about four feet and has smooth, large, dark-green leaves. At the joints of the leaves, growing upon stalks, are the bell-like flowers of a deadish purple, placed in a green husk and dented into five parts at the rims. After the flower comes a round berry with a crownlike form at its head. Inside is the purplish, winey liquor which we happily may never know.

Salmon again reminisces that when he was a child he ate one of the luscious berries. Luckily, its mawkish taste kept him from nibbling further. An eighteenth-century lad, known to that great herbalist William Curtis, when asked if he ate those wild berries, answered, "Yes, but it was naughty man's cherries." One of them won't poison you, but many will.

During the Industrial Revolution there was a real rage of new buildings in London, which did away with most of the deadly nightshade growing wild in lots and earthen areaways. Now one has to go out into the countryside to find it growing wild.

Not long before William the Conqueror, in the reign of Duncan I, king of Scotland (afterwards murdered by Macbeth), England

was invaded by the Danes. The Scots and the Danes battled fearfully; the Scots wanted men and the Danes provisions. A reenforcement of warriors could not be raised by the Scots, so that the armistice and the articles of peace were a welcome truce. On the becalmed battlefield the Scots were canny. They gave the Danes all manner of wines and ales, and gently mixed in neat quantities of that purplish liquor from the deadly nightshade. The bait took: the Danes drank plentifully and were all intoxicated, mad with the poisonous juice and asleep through drunkenness. Then the Scots descended and killed nearly all of them. With great effort, a few last Danes struggled to their ships, carrying their besotted king like a sack upon a beast. There were scarcely enough sailors left after the slaughter to man the ships and sail away.

Some substances, in large quantities or when injudiciously administered, have proved poisonous, but in small doses, skillfully employed, they have proved effective in various diseases. Belladonna, a medicine for heart disease, is processed from a bit of the liquid of deadly nightshade. Digitalis, effective in the treatment of a bad heart, is expressed from the poisonous but beautiful foxglove.

As an antidote, vinegar or tartar works well (if working well can be said about anything to do with deadly nightshade). The antidote has to be in good quantities to lessen the effects of the poison and then it helps by causing vomiting.

VIII. MONKSHOOD

Every part of this plant is a powerful poison, particularly the root. Its action is so rapid that an effective remedy cannot always be administered. With unknowing culinary gardeners, the young leaves can be mistaken for salad greens or parsley, and the root for horseradish. The root of monkshood has an earthy smell and is bitter to the taste. It is thick and blackish brown on the outside and white within. Knotty the root is, and it has many hairs and thready strings or strapes attached. A small carrot root or turnip bears a resemblance to monkshood's root.

This perennial is seen growing in circular patches or clusters with its bright-green, jagged, notched and slit leaves, lanceolate in form. The stems or stalks rise up about three feet and are hollow and wide. The stem is usually divided into two or three branches with a like number of leaves and a large, irregular and showy flower. The shape is very much like a hood, cowl, or better yet, an open helmet. Indeed, another name for this plant is helmet flower. There are a few small leaves at the sides of this helmet, closing it like cheeks, and two others which hang down like lobes. In the hollow of the blue flower grow two small crooked hairs like a wispy beard, and at their ends are little prickles or points. A little tail hangs behind the flower like a knight's spur. When the flowers fall and the crest of the helmet is gone, pods appear with hard, black, cornered seeds.

The plant is without any very remarkable pungency at first taste but soon produces a slight tingling and burning sensation attended with a kind of numbness and contraction of the skin of the tongue and roof of the mouth. The prickling or tingling soon extends over the body, and a feeling of constriction about the throat, occasionally amounting almost to strangling, causes the victim to clutch at his neck, and clench his fists and jaw convulsively. The time of death varies from one to eight hours after the poison has been swallowed.

Monkshood was introduced as a garden ornament or, more probably, as a powerful medicinal agent, at a very early period, and occupies at present a place in our materia medica.

The ancients regarded aconite (monkshood) as the most virulent of all poisons. Their mythologists declared it to be the invention of Hecate, who caused the plant to spring from the foaming slaver of many-headed Cerberus, when Hercules dragged him from the gloomy regions of Pluto. Medea put liquid from monkshood in a cup to poison Theseus. It was the draught that was given to those old men on the Aegean island of Keos when they were too feeble to be of further working value. The legends are thus told by Ovid:

Medea, to dispatch a dang'rous heir,
(She knew him) did a pois'nous draught prepare,
Drawn from a drug, long while reserved in store,
For desp'rate uses, from the Scythian shore,
That from the Echydnaean monster's jaws
Derived its origin, and this the cause.

Through a dark cave a craggy passage lies
To ours ascending from the nether skies,
Through which, by strength of hand, Alcides drew
Chained Cerberus, who lagged and restive grew,
With his bleared eyes our brighter day to view,
Thrice he repeated his enormous yell,
With which he scares the ghosts, and startles hell;
At last outrageous (though compelled to yield),
He sheds his foam in fury on the field;
Which, with its own and rankness of the ground,
Produced a weed by sorcerers renowned
The strongest constitution to confound—
Called Aconite, because it can unlock
All bars, and force its passage through a rock.

IX. POTATO AND MANIOC

Two very important and excellent food substances which at various times of their growth bear evidence of the surprising presence of poison in familiar plants are a South American cereal and — lo and behold — the common potato. (*Solanum tuberosum* is its botanic name; batata it was once called in England.)

The potato resembles the dangerous nightshade — which it is; also its white seeds look like those of that atrocious plant. But the danger lies in the flower, the leaf, and the stem, not the ripe tuber.

The root of the potato, dirty brown and whitish, is big as a wal-

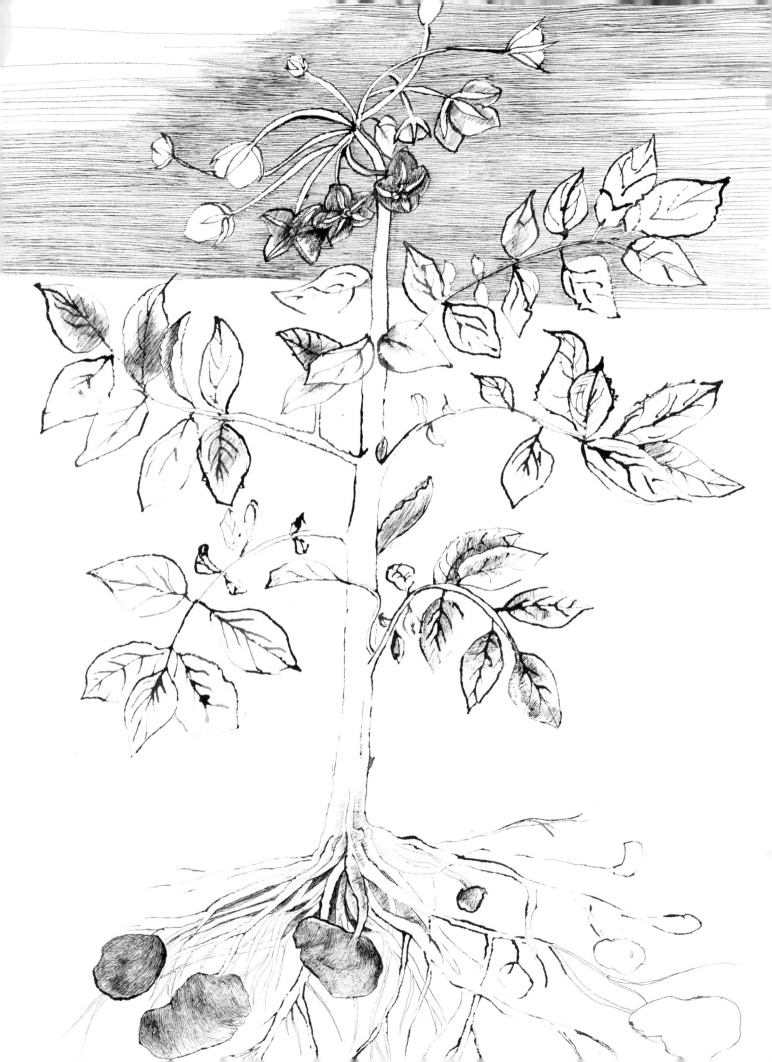

nut and somewhat knobby. From it grow many weak branches, easily wind-bent, with dove-colored, winged leaves, six-pointed at the brim. Between the leaves, with their reddish-yellow threads and thick golden pointlets tipped with green, rise up long stalks. The small white flowers, rimmed with green and pointed upward, look a good deal like those of tobacco. The berries or fruit are as large as damson plums. After they have fallen the noxious young green tuber begins to swell below ground but luckily it mellows into the luscious potato.

The potato was originally indigenous to Peru and Chile, was introduced into Spain about the beginning of the sixteenth century, and into England from Virginia in 1586 by Sir Walter Raleigh. Now, of course, it is cultivated everywhere.

Just as the potato is a vital food, so also is manioc, a prized Brazilian plant. Darwin, in *The Voyage of the Beagle,* describes this farinacious but deadly cereal: "Mandioca or Cassada is likewise cultivated in great quantity. Every part of this plant is useful: the leaves and stalks are eaten by the horses, and the roots are ground into a pulp, which when pressed dry and baked, forms the farinha, the principal article of sustenance in the Brazils. It is a curious, though well-known fact, that the juice of this most nutritious plant is highly poisonous."

X. HENBANE

Henbane has long been known as a poisonous plant. Nicander of Colophon (second century B.C.) wrote two treatises on poisons and in one of them described the effect of henbane. During the time of the temple in Israel a Hebrew high priest's miter was adorned, for certain occasions, with a chaplet of the blossoms of henbane. According to an old German belief, henbane is said to attract rain and produce sterility. There is a curious old tradition in Piedmont that if a hare be sprinkled with henbane juice all the other hares in the neighborhood will run away as if scared by some invisible power.

There are some quite ludicrous tales told about this narcotic plant, for instance, that its roots were eaten for supper by the monks of a

monastery, who thought it an esculent vegetable. All who had partaken were more or less affected during the night and the following day. One monk got up at midnight and tolled the bell for matins, while of those who obeyed the summons, some could not read, others repeated what was not in their breviaries, and many were seized with the strangest hallucinations.

Gerard gives us a "recipe" for using henbane: "The root, boiled with vinegar, and the same holden hot in the mouth, easeth the pain of the teeth. The seed is used by mountebank tooth-drawers, which run about the country, to cause worms to come forth of the teeth, by burning it in a chafing-dish of coles, the party holding his mouth over the fumes thereof; but some crafty companions, to gain money, convey small lute-strings into the water, persuading the patient that those small creepers came out of his mouth or other parts which he intended to cure." Even in a nineteenth-century herbal, henbane is still mentioned as a fix-it-all for toothache.

Henbane, both yellow and black, grows in dry waste ground and on rubbish heaps. It is a low plant, growing a few inches to a foot or more in height. The leaves are clammy-pubescent, wooly and hirsute, and the stems are downy and hairy. The plant has a strongly fetid odor. When damp, its aroma is tobacco-like and it is bitter-tasting. The flowers are greenish-yellow generally, with dark-purple veins forming a network over the corolla. The leaves are jagged and angled, the upper leaf clasping. In July and August come the blossoms, bell-shaped, urnlike or funnel-formed. When the flowers fall off, they are followed by round husks, like a collection of pots covered with small lids, enclosed with rough skins, the whole looking like a cluster of helmets. These pots are set in a row one after another along the stalks. Within them are brown seeds.

Baleful draughts of witch's brew can be made from henbane, about which Ben Jonson writes in his *Masque of Queens:*

> *And I ha' been plucking plants among*
> *Hemlock, Henbane, Adder's Tongue;*
> *Nightshade, Moonwort, Libbard's bane,*
> *And twice, by the dogs, was like to be ta'en.*

XI. PASSIONFLOWER

Around Easter blooms the passionflower. Because it was Easter-time when Christ was crucified, the varied marks on the flower's innocent face are looked upon as a sign of Christ's Passion. In French, both Easter and Passover (Pesach) are called *Pâque,* in English Pasque, another name for the passionflower. In Latin, it is *pulsatilla.*

The root lies deep in the ground (not just underneath the crust of earth as with many other plants); it is long and thick, and at its top is a tuft of hair like a bushy beard. Lying upon the earth, flopping, there are many winged leaves, hairy, rough and hard, but finely cut into, of a dark-green color, shredded about, and looking like a carrot's leaves but finer, from which rise up naked, fuzzy footstalks about a span high. Then on the top of each stalk is a hanging, bell-shaped flower, and set in the midst of each is a tuft of grassy yellow threads, close around a kind of stylus or stiletto in the center of each bloom.

The colors of the flower resemble those of the rainbow —blue, red, yellow, white and the favorite of all, purple.

When the flower is gone there comes a velvety head or knob, with a hoary, tresslike structure, filled with whitish, long, flat, thin seeds, each with tiny gray hairs attached to it. It is not only the seeds that are poisonous but the entire plant including the pretty flower.

When a person comes to his end because of the passionflower, it is said that he "dies laughing." The nerves of his mouth, jaws and eyes are wrung and drawn awry and he dies from terrible torturous pain and murderous convulsions, yet his face is wrenched into a smile. The onlookers think that the dying man is just in a silly mood or laughing humor but what they see is really the oncoming, unholy death.

The Mexican Jesuit Jacomo Bosio felt the passionflower to symbolize Christ's veritable suffering, finding its flower to represent mystically His crown of thorns, as well as the sponge to wipe His face, the evil scourge, the nails, then down unto His five bloody

wounds coming from the dark stamens. And so all these inflorescent parts are seen as miraculous.

An insipid yellow fruit, known as the maracock or maypop, follows the flower.

When the plant is being botanically pressed, its splashed juices and its strong vapor momentarily and painfully close the eyes of anyone handling it.

XII. JACK-IN-THE-PULPIT

Cuckoopint, lords-and-ladies and wake-robin are some other names for Jack-in-the-Pulpit. The root is tuberous with a round swelling as big as a walnut. If it is chewed, it has an acrid taste like pepper. Its juice, rather like a clammy, pithy paste, is often used as a starch even though it smarts the hands. The root is green without and white within and somewhat thready. Unlike other flowers, one cannot say it waves in the wind, for it stands erect like a stalwart stanchion. Because of this it is mythically called *Canis Priapus*. It has green arrow-shaped leaves stained with purple speckles and it contains a large, sheathlike spathe with a wan, purplish spike open like a hare's ear.

The plant rises brightly in the early spring in marshes, the flowers ultimately wither, and clusters of yellowish red berries, as big as hazelnuts, follow in the summer. The tall unit of the plant reminds one of a pestle, clapper or hose. The columnar, club-shaped flower is formed like a turnip.

The leaf is forked, as that of the wild sorrel, with a naked, round, greenish-white, pointed stalk. This stalk is spotted or straked with purple like unto the dragon stalk, and it pushes up somewhat higher than the leaves. These leaves become crumpled and shriveled, suggesting a paper bag, but there are others that grow under the loose ones with many fibers hanging firm. Its poisonous properties lie in the rhizome or root structure.

The Germans had the notion that where the Jack-in-the-Pulpit flourished the spirits of the woods would rejoice. The grand Ethio-

pian kind is usually called the horn-flower from the shape of its white whorl of leaves. The English call it a batch of names, including cows-and-calves, friar's-cowl, parson-in-the-pulpit, priest's-hood, devil's pintle, ramp and starchwort. And, of course, it got its favorite name, "cuckoopint," because it is a "harbinger of spring" and appears when the cuckoo sings its song. Because of its Latin name, *Arum*, it was mistakenly called by the Hebrew name of Aaron. The blood that seemingly spilled over the Cross (because of the red berries that surround the center) gave it the name of Gethsemane. So this poem:

Those deep inwrought marks,
The villagers will tell thee,
Are the flower's portion from the atoning blood
On Calvary shed. Beneath the Cross it grew.

The bitter juice expressed from the plant contains a farinacious substance good to eat: in England it is sold under the name of Portland Sago. The French use a bit of the root in a cosmetic called Cypress Powder. A sure remedy for the once-upon-a-time plague was a drachm-weight either dry or fresh. And a spoonful of the juice, swallowed, was said to have the same effect. When the berries or the roots are beaten up with oxdung, the potion supposedly cures gout.

Astrologically, Jack-in-the-Pulpit comes under the mystic sign of Mars.

And the great Thomas Hardy has this to say: "The odd cuckoopint like an apoplectic saint in a niche of malachite."

XIII. RUSH

The root of the rush is bushy, spreading and creeping, stringy and intricately fibrous. The plant has a tuft or umbel with a brownish, sparse panicle rising upward, long and pointed. The rush is tallish, hard, sharp and spearlike with whitish, pithy shoots and smooth stalks, hollow, porous and spongy. The rush has two short leaves and several chaffy husks looking very much like brown reed grass. It has a skinny, slender head like a little button, which contains the seeds with reddish skins. These seeds bear at their tops a small catkin or aglet, like the first head of an asparagus, blooming with small white threads, which quickly fall away.

The rush has pale-blue flowers, some tipped with yellow in the middle. When they are gone there come in their places small, round, blackish heads, within them small seeds.

Some call the rush by other names—sea grass or marsh grass or goose corn, but all the rushes comprise a great family called in Latin *Juncaceae*. The leaves of the *Juncus inflexus* can be very dangerous to animals. From all of the rushes can be distilled a powerful narcotic.

It springs up in overgrown fields, waste ground, and the margins of highways, waving wildly wheatlike in the breeze and sun. It also likes the wetness of moors, swamps, marshy and plashy grounds, and of fenny, miry ditches.

There is a little lore about the strutting and long-legged rush. Here is a long and sad story: The sea-nymph Galatea was enamored of Acis, a young sheepherder of Sicily, who sweetly reciprocated her love. Unluckily, Galatea was adored by the Cyclops Polyphemus, whom she hated. Once the Cyclops caught the sweethearts together and they ran away from his suspicious, terrible anger. The giant, however, tossed a great fistful of smashed stones at Acis, which pounded him to death. Galatea, much saddened by the loss of her lover, decided to convert him into a stream, through magic. The blood of the crushed shepherd, coming from a bit of the stone which had killed him, slowly became a running watercourse. And so this poem:

> The stone was cleft, and through the yawning chink
> New Reeds arose on the new river's brink;
> The rock from out its hollow womb disclosed
> A sound like water in its course opposed.
> When (wondrous to behold) full in the flood

Up starts a youth, and navel-high he stood.
Horns from his temples rise; and either horn
Thick wreaths of Reeds (his native growth) adorn.

So the flowering rush was thought to sprout from the blood of Acis.

The flower now called Acis is actually a dwarf amaryllid. People used to call it in Latin *Juncus floridus,* and Gerard named it the water gladiole.

When high holy days came around it was usual to adorn the floors of churches with flowering branches, herbs and rushes. This custom existed when William the Conqueror was born. Upon seeing with bright open eyes that the floor was covered with sprigs and rushes, he bent, the tottering infant, and grasped in his hand, and would not let go, bunches of sweet-smelling rushes. This was taken as an omen that William would be the future king. During Elizabeth's reign, in Shakespeare's plays, we find many references to the custom of spilling rushes on the ground for their gentle odor.

Newton, a sixteenth-century botanist, writes this in his book, *Herbal to the Bible:* "Sedge and rushes, with which many in the country do use in summer time to strewe their parlors and churches, as well for coolness and for pleasant smell." Cardinal Wolsey, at his prideful zenith, liked to coat the floor of the great hall at Hampton Court with rushes and other fragrant herbs, refreshing them every day. In Yorkshire, Cheshire and Westmoreland, the ancient rite of rush-bearing is followed even to this day; it is nothing but the olden celebration of bearing rushes to decorate the church on the Feast of Dedication and on other holy days.

Virgil anointed Dante with the rush in *The Divine Comedy.* The reedmace (the rush) is depicted by Rubens, as well as by early Italian painters, as the rod given to Christ to carry, and it is still put by Catholics into the hands of statues of Christ. But in Poland, where the plant is difficult to procure, the flowerstalk of the leek is substituted.

The poet Francis Quarles writes in his "Sheapheard's Oracles":

Love-sick swains
Composed rush-rings and myrtle-berry chains,
And stuck with glorious kingcups, and their bonnets
Adorn'd with laurel slips, chaunt their love sonnets.

XIV. THORN APPLE

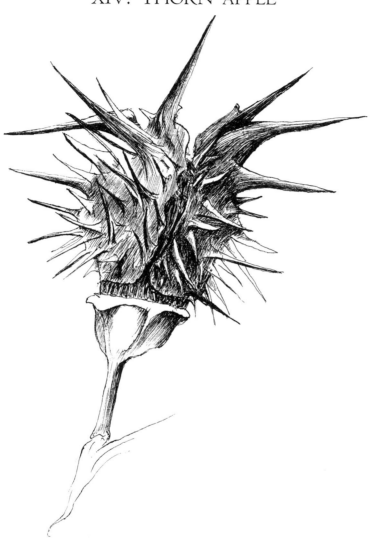

Our summer place in Maine sits near the water where there are thorn-apple "trees." The last word is in quotes, for although the thorn apple looks like a young apple tree, it is really a shrub. Any tree-shrub with berries and spikes may be, typically, called "thorn apple," even unto the hawthorn with its fruit and furious thorns.

The thorn apple has one great central stalk about seven feet high, quite thick in diameter, and with many branches. The leaf is smooth, very broad, jagged about the edges, and looks like spinach. The flowers come forth from long-toothed cups, great and white, formed like bells or trumpets. They look like the blooms of the great bindweed, but are wider at the mouth and more sharp-cornered at the brim. After the flower dies, then comes the prickly black and brown many-seeded fruit looking much like a small walnut.

The fruit has a strong smell, causing drowsiness. In the recent past, a scientist, examining the fresh plant for a materia medica, relates that the narcotic effluvia affected him so powerfully he became slightly intoxicated. The thorn apple also contains good drugs like atropin belladonna, which we met before when we talked about deadly nightshade.

The patient, worrying about an operation, can look forward to becoming anesthetized and sleeping painlessly upon taking an extract of the thorn apple. If you try to walk a bit after taking in some of this plant, you stagger about as if dancing drunk. Speaking of drunkenness, it is said that the Chinese are legally forbidden to imbibe thorn-apple juice, for which they have a taste.

The plant has a number of names, most of them nicknames coming from children, like devil's-apple, and earnest names like jimson-weed, angel's-trumpet, or night-blooming cactus. But it is best to call the thorn apple by its Latin name of *Datura stramonium*.

The name jimsonweed is a corruption of its older name, Jamestown weed. Historians tell us that soldiers in the Virginia uprising of 1676 known as Bacon's Rebellion, which occurred in Jamestown, unfortunately ate the berries of this plant when they had nothing else to eat and, of course, became deathly ill.

Thoreau tells us in his *Cape Cod* that the *Datura stramonium* grows wild along the shore. In a wondrous footnote, he quotes from Beverly's *History of Virginia*, as follows:

"The Jamestown weed (or thorn-apple). 'This, being an early plant, was gathered very young for a boiled salad, by some of the soldiers sent thither [i.e., to Virginia] to quell the rebellion of Bacon; and some of them ate plentifully of it, the effect of which was a very pleasant comedy, for they turned natural fools upon it for several days: one would blow up a feather in the air; another would dart straws at it with much fury; and another, stark naked, was sitting up in a corner like a monkey, grinning and making mows at them; a fourth would fondly kiss and paw his companions, and sneer in their faces, with a countenance more antic than any in a Dutch droll. In this frantic condition they were confined, least they should, in their folly, destroy themselves,—though it was observed that all their actions were full of innocence and good nature. Indeed, they were not very cleanly. A thousand such simple tricks they played, and after eleven days returned to themselves again, not remembering anything that had passed.'"

Children are endlessly wandering into thickets of thorn apple, eating its seeds and sometimes dying. Two boys were playing in a New York City lot where the *Datura* was luxuriantly growing, as it does in many city lots. They imagined themselves Indians and roamed about eating various plants until they hit upon the thorn apple, which brought their games to a terrible end.

In Greece, in an early century, the Delphic priests, by taking the *Datura,* would produce those semidelirious paroxysms which they palmed off on the multitude as the manifestations of divine inspiration. Matthiolus, a sixteenth-century herbalist, thinks the thorn apple to be the *nux methel* of the Arabians. More recently, in the New World, the California Indians would give their children narcotic potions of the *Datura* to gain from the ensuing visions information about their enemies as well as prophetic delirium in which hidden treasure was revealed. Similarly, the Delaware medicine men used to drink thorn apple decoctions until their minds became bewildered and they saw extraordinary visions.

ADDENDA: NOTES ON A HUNDRED MORE

We have written a good deal about some of the important plants deadly to people. Often, close relatives of these plants (sometimes beautiful and familiar ones), ground into ensilage or growing in meadows, sicken or kill unsuspecting cattle. Here briefly are a hundred plants, of lesser importance but overlooked only at one's peril, whose chief victims are human beings:

1. *Absinthe or Common Wormwood.* Absinthe is often added to hops to make the beer more palatable. People who drink absinthe suffer a loss of memory—called "absinthe epilepsy."

2. *African Marigold.* The lesser, single one has a stinking smell unlike the double flower. The leaves are hollow and cavernous, thin and winged, like those of an ash tree.

3. *Akee.* Clusters of the leathery-skinned fruit are formed about twice a year. Parboiling and frying give it a somewhat nutty flavor. The seed is poisonous.

4. *Apple Seeds.* A windfall of apples is great fun, but watch out for the seeds! A man once thought a cupful of them a great delicacy but died of cyanide poisoning.

5. *Barberry.* Some of the North American species are weedy, others woody. This plant is in many pharmacopoeias.

6. *Bittersweet.* It is listed as poisonous, but its principle has not been identified. Children must watch out for its candylike berry decorating the house, come wintertime.

7. *Black Bryony.* The scraped root is used to remove discoloration from bruises, so it is also called blackeye root. The berry is bright-red and fleshy.

8. *Bloodroot.* From the red root. So acid, one has to be heroic to chew and swallow it.

9. *Blue Cohosh.* Used as a fish poison. Asthenically it acts on the heart.

10. *Bulbous Buttercup.* In England children have been poisoned by

this plant, mistaking it for pignuts. Foraging animals reject it unless nothing else is about.

11. *Caper Spurge.* The whole plant is covered with a whitish "bloom" like that on plums and grapes. Often the fruit is pickled and used for capers.

12. *Castor-oil Plant.* A purgative hated by children. Originally native to Asia, yet having a poison more serious than prussic acid or strychnine.

13. *Celandine.* Its yellowish liquid tastes like mustard, but it relates to bloodroot. It is medicinally valuable and expensive.

14. *Cherrystones.* Contain prussic acid. Luckily, breaking them is a bit difficult. A cold stream of water poured downward on the head and spine is quite a good antidote, strangely.

15. *Chokecherry.* The ripe fruit goes from dark purple to near black. The berries make a good preserve, attractive to children —but stay away from the horrid pits.

16. *Clammy Locust.* The bark and leaves are the chief danger, though honey from the nectar of the flower can do harm too. The poison is a lot like belladonna.

17. *Cocaine.* When cocaine touches the skin it is bad. One-half a grain, given subcutaneously, killed a child in little more than forty seconds.

18. *Common Elder.* Wood very pithy and quite porous. Its acid is strong when it is young and weak when it is old. A wonderful wine is made from the berries.

19. *Common Privet.* The familiar suburban hedge. The flowers ripen into a drooping cluster of black or blue wax-coated berries. The leaf is poisonous.

20. *Corn Cockle.* This plant grows on wheat-fattened soil and woe to us when it gets mixed into our bread. It contains the noxious saponin.

21. *Cowbane.* A resinous substance with a sharp taste. The poison resides in all parts, the root, stem and leaves, but especially in the root.

22. *Crab's Eye Vine, Rosary Pea.* The black marking that covers the tip of the seed shows its scar of attachment; the seed looks as if it has been dipped in black enamel.
23. *Cursed Crowfoot.* It grows luxuriantly in close-cropped pastures. Leaves, flowers and stems have a peppery and pungent taste like mustard.
24. *Custard-apple Family.* Most alkaloids taste bad but these are tasteless. Care should be exercised in their necessary medicinal use.
25. *Daphne, Mezereum.* The berries are scarlet, contrasting with the green herbage. Their effect on the nervous system is akin to that of monkshood and deadly nightshade.
26. *Deadly Amanita.* This is a wild mushroom and, of course, all wild mushrooms are forbidden to eat. It causes weakness and a peculiar yellowing of the face.
27. *Delphinium.* Grows in the spring when the grass is newly green. The upper petals form a long spur and there are many seeded, baglike fruits.
28. *Dog's Bane.* Suckers adhere to the roots. In America it is often called Virginia Silk.
29. *Dog's Mercury.* Touch-me-not and quick-seed it is also called, for indeed its dusky seeds are wafted from their pods by the slightest breeze.
30. *English Ivy.* Since Pliny, it has been considered evil. When the leaves are ingested the poisoning starts with excitement —then breathless coma, then death.
31. *European Beech.* This tree should not be mistaken for the American beech, which it resembles. The deadly seeds, made into oily cakes, can kill animals.
32. *Fava Beans.* Inhaling the pollen is toxically shattering, especially to persons who have a low red-blood-cell count. Males are affected more than females.
33. *Filicales.* The leaves of this fern are rolled up in the bud and the spores at the back of the frond break open and are discharged.

34. *Fool's Parsley.* Causes anxiety, hiccough and a delirium that can last for as long as three months. It is fatal to geese.

35. *Foxglove.* The bell-shaped flower gives us the medicine, digitalis, that strengthens the heartbeat.

36. *Golden Dewdrop.* A small shrub which contains saponic principles and is suspected of causing death to livestock in Australia.

37. *Great Angelica.* Canadian Indians use the fresh root to commit suicide, although the stems are often made into a candied preserve in some parts of Canada.

38. *Greensauce Sorrel.* A lot like the knot-grass tribe, and the leaves work well as salad greens. English apothecaries sell it as "essential salt of lemon." The liquid in the stalk is harmful.

39. *Groundsel, Senecio.* Where death from this plant is suspected, a taxonomic botanist must be consulted. Usually has a single whorl, occasionally an overlapping one.

40. *Hawthorn, or Whitethorn.* Death from the fruit often comes from strangulation by the stony seed; the flesh is very indigestible.

41. *Hemp.* Both sexes have flowers; only the female has seeds. Hemp cordage can be sucked, but not the flower.

42. *Herb Christopher.* Resembles bindweed; it has grapelike berries along the viny stem.

43. *Herb Paris, Truelove.* A four-petaled, star-shaped green flower rises up on its tall stem, followed by a bluish-purple berry.

44. *Horse Chestnut.* Children often mistake horse chestnut for real chestnut. Beware!

45. *Horsetail.* The blackish roots of this rushlike perennial are in whorls from the node.

46. *Hound's-tongue.* Resembles a dog's tongue, so its name; but it has the smell of a mouse.

47. *Indian Tobacco.* The flowers grow within a capsule, and it has the slang name of pukeweed. The leaves are dentate and enclosed in a bract.

48. *Jerusalem Cherry.* This common pot plant, a vicious solanum, has succulent, bright-red berries. It is prized for ornamental reasons, but children must be cautious.

49. *Kentucky Coffee Tree.* Often mistaken for the honey locust when it sprouts from cut-over lands. It is badly toxic.

50. *Laburnum.* The golden rain of its flower is something like yellow wisteria. The fruit resembles string beans.

51. *Lantana.* The berries are considered to be lethal. The animal eating them becomes photosensitized and its skin may erupt.

52. *Larkspur.* Has a fascicled tubular root and Pliny says its powdered seeds help cure pediculosis.

53. *Leopard's-bane.* Supposedly, wild animals like wolves and leopards can be slain by arrows dipped in this poison—so says Pliny, so its name.

54. *Licorice Root.* Grows in the warmer regions of Europe and Asia and is used to hide the taste of nauseating medicine; it contains glucoside.

55. *Lily of the Valley.* A lot like foxglove and related to the aloes that give us onions and wild garlic.

56. *Lupine.* This herbaceous plant occasionally grows as a shrub on sandy soil. In Europe the seed is often used as a coffee substitute.

57. *Magnolia Family.* The magnolia, sometimes an evergreen, grows near Buddhist temples in Japan. Perfume is made from the flowers.

58. *Maidenhair Fern.* The root stock is slender and chaffy; the stalk, black and shiny, is forked at the summit.

59. *Meadow Saffron.* Colchicum it is also called, from ancient Colchis, on the Black Sea, where it grew wild.

60. *Mescal Bean.* Grows in canyons, such as the Grand Canyon. One masticated seed is a lethal dose. Sometimes its leaflet tip is retuse (not obtuse).

61. *Milkweed.* The leaves are whorled, the seeds flat with tufts of hair called a coma, the flowers in umbels and urn-shaped. The fruit has a milky juice.

62. *Mistletoe.* With its pinkish-white berries it covers oak trees and sometimes kills them. The tea brewed from the berries of this Christmas plant is fatal.

63. *Mountain Laurel.* Deer and ordinary grouse are immune to it; but for ruffed grouse it is poisonous. Its honey is harmful.

64. *Mustard* or *English Charlock.* Its flowers are large, yellow, and very fragrant. A poultice should not be placed on a woman's chest because it turns the skin brown.

65. *Night-blooming* and *Day-blooming Jessamine* (jasmine). Flowers greenish-white, and, according to type, sweet-scented by day or night. It poisons like atropine.

66. *Night-flowering Catchfly.* A viscid hairy annual with sweet-smelling flowers which bloom at night; it has smallish, kidney-shaped, black seeds.

67. *Oleander.* In Spain there is a story told that, when spits were made from this plant on which to roast an animal, many soldiers died from the peeled stems.

68. *Orpine Family.* Grows only at the Cape of Good Hope. Poisoning results even from the smell. It produces the Nenta disease and also loco.

69. *Pinkroot.* It has sessile leaves and slender, tubular, funnel-formed petals. A powerful worm-killer, it contains a volatile alkaloid.

70. *Poinsettia.* This ornamental plant is used for Christmas because of its red leaves; the flowers are small and yellow-red.

71. *Pokeweed.* Also called inkberry. It has white flowers and a purple, juicy berry. The young shoots of this perennial are betimes taken for asparagus.

72. *Puffed-up Lobelia.* Homeopathic doctors often cure spasmodic asthma by using this plant—a stout and hairy perennial with thin acute leaves.

73. *Purging Buckthorn.* The juice of the fleshy fruit is used for staining maps and the dye of the fruit for paints.

74. *Ragged Robin.* The leaves of this downy, branching, hairy perennial are lanceolate. The flowers—red, white and bluish—rise up in panicles.

75. *Rattlebox.* We have to beware, for its seeds, which rattle when shaken, contaminate flour as often as they do corn, peas and soybeans.

76. *Rhododendron.* A great open tree or evergreen shrub; the corolla is bell-shaped and deeply lobed.
77. *Rhubarb.* The stalks are good to eat, but the leaf is devilish. In England, during the war, it was stupidly recommended that the plant be eaten.
78. *Rosebay.* This plant is related to the genus *Azalea.* It has flowers that grow in a cluster with scaly conelike buds.
79. *Rubber Vine.* Leathery-leaved and thick-stemmed is this woody vine, naturalized on roadsides and in waste soils. Once it killed a monkey.
80. *Santalales.* Same family as mistletoe and fragrant sandalwood. A semiparasitic plant, its oil is used for perfume and to cure venereal disease.
81. *Sea Island Cotton.* Used in the manufacture of cottonseed oil. A highly explosive guncotton is made by soaking it in sulfuric and nitric acid.
82. *Sea Lungwort.* Beloved of snails and slugs, this plant sends its roots deep into the sand.
83. *Silverleaf Psoralea.* Silvery with pubescent and appressed hairs; the stem is zigzag.
84. *Star-of-Bethlehem.* The onion-like bulbs are often brought to the surface by frost heaves, plowing, or by hogs rooting in the ground.
85. *Tall Gypsophyla.* A pubescent perennial having a simple spindle-shaped root and white or pink flowers with thorny margins.
86. *Tansey.* Tansey tea is often taken to relieve painful menstruation. Oil of tansey has been used as a worm-killer since the Middle Ages.
87. *Tobacco.* This plant of the family *Solanacea,* when still fresh, is very evil; when dried and cured it can be smoked and chewed.
88. *Trumpet Flower* or *Chalice Vine.* Generally cultivated in greenhouses or in the warmer parts of the United States. Showy white or yellow flowers grace it.
89. *Vetchling* or *Flat Pea.* Disease and death from this plant have

been noted since Hippocrates. Poverty and drought make people eat its seeds.

90. *Violet Wood Sorrel.* The leaves and the raw herb throw children into convulsions. It is a perennial with a brownish bulb and ciliate scales.

91. *Water Dropwort.* Stains the hands with a yellow juice. When not in flower bears a strong resemblance to celery and its root to parsnip.

92. *White Snakeroot.* Milk-sickness affects the dairy products and meat of animals that have fed upon it. The leaves are sharply and coarsely toothed.

93. *Wild Red Cherry.* Watch out when the leaf is cut and wilted. The stones are devilish, full of prussic acid, smelling and tasting like bitter almond.

94. *Wisteria.* One or two seeds from this purple pearl of a flower are very harmful. People who eat them are often put on the critical list.

95. *Wolfsbane.* The root is a lot like that of the anemone and the plant rises in the wintertime with snow on its leaves; the flower reminds one of crowfoot.

96. *Wood Anemone.* The root grows obliquely under the surface of the earth and has the thickness of a crow quill.

97. *Wormseed.* Also called goosefoot, and no wonder, since geese love it. Anthelmintic oil in the plant is the harsh element.

98. *Yellow Jessamine.* Climbs over shrubs and trees as high as thirty feet. The root is often used in medicine, and overdoses are common.

99. *Yew.* The flowers of this conifer grow in scaly bracts near small-ish catkins, subtended by fleshy cup-shaped disks.

100. *Yucca.* This South American hemplike growth has prickly, sharp-pointed leaves that cut like a knife. The plant is used to make bread.

"Have we eaten of the insane root
That takes the reason prisoner?"

MACBETH